30

First New England Press edition 1983
Second printing, September 1984
Third printing, April 1988
ISBN 0-933050-18-6

(Previously published by Lanser Press
ISBN 0-9603900-5-7)

Other books by Jeff Danziger

The Vermont Mind
Completely Undercoated Cartoons
The Wood-fired Automobile
The Champlain Monster
Out in the Sticks II
Out in the Sticks III

Copies may be obtained from

The New England Press, Inc.
P.O. Box 575
Shelburne, Vermont 05482

Danziger's
THE
ILLUSTRATED

UNOFFICIAL

HUNTING
RULES

The New England Press
Shelburne, Vermont

Preface or Introduction or Whatever ...

There are probably as many unofficial rules of hunting as there are official rules of hunting, and many times the unofficial rules, based in tradition and experience are more important than the official ones. We thank the many hunters who helped us pin down some of the less important ones. All of the important ones we left out.

This book is intended for the enjoyment of its readers; not one word in it should be taken seriously. It is dedicated to the many sportsmen who realize that respect for the outdoors is reflectively respect for themselves.

And we offer it to those who know that a sense of humor is needed by anyone who takes his sport seriously.

Rule 29 — Target Practice
Makes Perfect

SIGHTING-IN DIRECTIONS:

PIN BOOK OPEN TO THIS PAGE ON SIDE OF BARN

1st SHOT - NEW ENGLAND - GOOD

2nd SHOT - WITHIN STATE - GOOD

3rd SHOT - BROAD SIDE OF BARN - GOOD

4rd SHOT - BETWEEN TRACTOR AND MILKHOUSE - GREAT!

5th SHOT - INNER CIRCLE - EXCELLENT!

6th SHOT - BULL'S EYE -

PURE
LUCK...

Rule 7 — A Man's Camp is His Castle

Rule 2 — The Damn Deer Get Smarter Every Year

Rule 82 — Don't Neglect Your Diet

REMEMBER THE FOUR FOOD GROUPS!

1. VIENNA SAUSAGES
   YUM! CONTINENTAL DELICACIES MADE FROM FRESH SNOUTS, EARS AND BEEF LIPS.

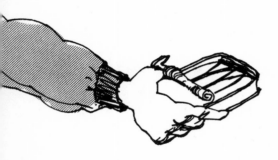

2. SARDINES
   GO PERFECT WITH VIENNA SAUSAGES FOR SURF 'N' TURF

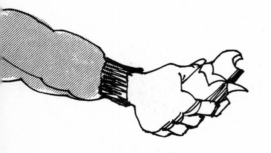

3. CANDY BARS
   THAT OLD AMERICAN FAVORITE! LIGHT UP YOUR FILLINGS.

4. CHEWING TOBACCO
   ENTERTAINING NOURISHMENT THAT SHARPENS YOUR AIM

MR. HIRAM TEED OF EAST WHITTLE DOWN
ENTERTAINS FELLOW HUNTERS WITH A CULINARY
MASTERPIECE: THE STATE SEAL OF VERMONT DONE
IN BEANS, FRANKS, SLIM JIMS, RAVIOLIS, RAISINS,
AND AMERICAN PROCESS CHEESE.

OLD NEW ENGLAND RECIPE
Venison Stew

5 LBS. DEER MEAT
3 QTS. BEER
1 QT. CHEAP SCOTCH
1 QT. RED WINE
1 QT. BOURBON

COOK 20 MINUTES
DISCARD MEAT
DRINK WHAT'S LEFT.

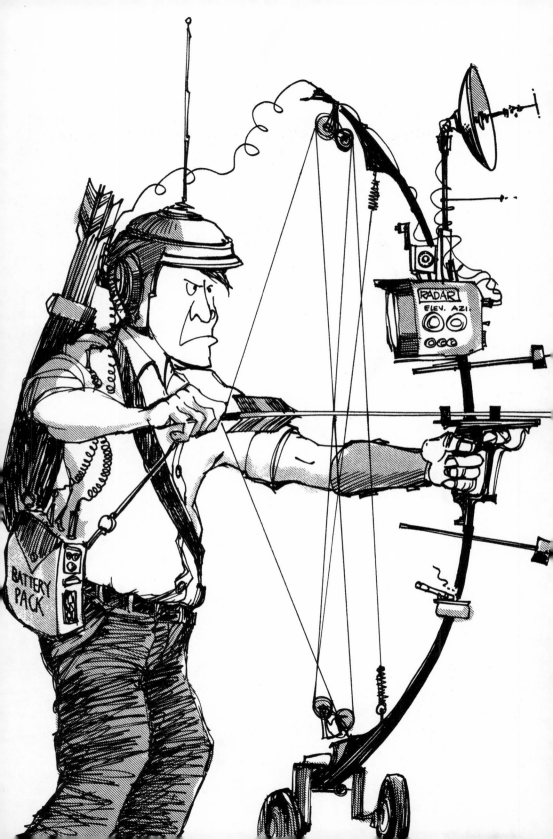

Rule 28 — The True Hunter Prefers to Hunt Like the Indians

Rule 91 — The Wise Landowner Only Posts Next Year's Firewood

Rule 64 — A Light Snowfall Makes Tracking Easier

Rule 473 — Never Hunt With a Vietnam Veteran Who is Still Eating C—rations (especially if he is still eating them with his fingers.)

Rule 14 — Be Prepared, But Not Too Prepared

Rule 59 — Give a Farmer a Break

EDWIN TOOMEY
(NOT GEORGE TOOMEY, THIS
IS EDWIN, GEORGE'S
BROTHER, EDWARD
WAS HIS COUSIN.)

REPORTS THIS IDEA
PROTECTS HIS STOCK
BETTER 'CAUSE
MOST HUNTERS
KNOW THEY CAN'T
HIT A CHICKEN..

Rule 503 — You are Allowed to Hold Up Traffic
Five Minutes for Every Car Behind You

Rule 3 —
Don't Reload if You Are Already Loaded

Rule 53 — There Are Safer Places Than a Safety Zone

Rule 47 — Blend With The Scenery

Rule 75 — There's More Than One Way to Harvest Corn

... Unless It's Being Caught in a Drive

Rule 41 — Don't Hang a Deer More Than Three
 Days, Even if All the Neighbors Haven't Seen It

Rule 81 — Don't Take Any More to Camp Than You Can Afford To Lose

Rule 58 — Don't Hunt With Cheapskates

Rule 45 — You Can Always Identify an Out—of—Stater

Rule 632 — Dress For The Weather

Rule 137 — Tree Stands Don't Fool Anybody

Rule 289 — It Is Illegal To Shoot At A Swimming Deer

Rule 467 — If God Meant Hunters to Be Comfortable,
He Wouldn't Have Invented Winter

Rule 20 — Advice Is Free
(and worth every penny)

Rule 534 — Get A Good Night's Sleep

Rule 412 — If You Have To Ask How Much Deer Meat Costs, You Can't Afford It

LICENSE	8.00
RIFLE	150.00
AMMO	15.00
GASOLINE	40.00
FOOD + BEVERAGES	50.00
SNACKS	50.00
CLOTHING	200.00
HOT SEAT	10.00
LOST BOOT (LEFT)	42.00
MORE BEVERAGES	20.00
CAMP MAINTENANCE	2.50
BATTERIES FOR ELECTRIC SOCKS	10.00
FLAT TIRE	25.00
BRIBE TO FARMER'S KID	8.00
TOW CHARGE	20.00
LOST KNIFE	18.00
MORE BEVERAGES	15.00
LOST PAY	200.00
BUTCHERING	40.00
GIFT FOR WIFE	1.95

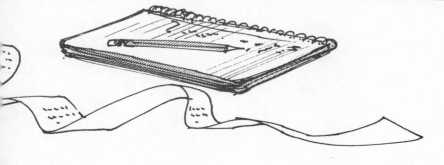